To Teach To Love

To Teach
To Love

Reflections Past and Present

MICHAEL FREELAND

Periploi Press / NASHVILLE

© 2012 Michael Freeland
All rights reserved

Published by Periploi Press
Nashville, Tennessee

ISBN 978-0-9830-1151-4
Library of Congress Control Number: 2012932674

Frontispiece: High school graduation picture,
Flora Ellen Elmore, 1948.
Text drawings by Michael Freeland

This book is printed on acid-free paper.
Printed in the United States by Thomson-Shore, Inc.
Designed by Dariel Mayer

ALSO BY MICHAEL FREELAND

Blood River to Berlin:
The World War II Journal
of an Army Medic

Time and the River:
A Memoir

Dedicated to Stephen Allen Freeland
March 2, 1954–September 2, 1979

Love is the emblem of
Eternity.
It confounds all notion
Of time,
Effaces all memory of a
Beginning
All fear of an end.
    —Germaine de Stael

Time flies
Suns rise
And shadows fall
Let time go by
Love is forever over all.
    —Author unknown

Quoted in a letter to the people of LaGrange,
Georgia; written by Mike and Ellen Freeland
after the death of their son Steve, 1979.

Also dedicated to these young poets

Amy Mason Symington Huskawisky
Patrick Mason Poe
Melissa Ellen Poe Hood
Jessie David Rudolph Freeland
John Hargis Noel Freeland
Lindsay Katherine Freeland
Graham Lucas Freeland
Ashley Gail Freeland
Tyler Lee Freeland
Andrew Thomas Freeland
Emma Larissa Huskawisky
Luke Mason Huskawisky
James Montgomery Hood
Shyanne Lynn Freeland
Amelia Ellen Hood
Alice Bolling Poe

And for my children:

Cynthia Grey Freeland Symington
Michael Rudolph Freeland, Jr.
Patricia Sharon Freeland Poe
Stephen Allen Freeland
Douglas Lee Freeland
David Elmore Freeland

Contents

In Appreciation

> As for man, his days are like grass.
> He flourishes like a flower of the field.
> For the wind passes over it,
> and it is gone and its place
> knows it no more.
>   —*Psalm 103, 15*

To Teach to Love is my labor of love and appreciation for the story-tellers included here, as well as all those countless other writers and teachers I appreciate. It is, at least, an acknowledgement of the debt I can never repay. I remember first the old storytellers, my grandparents, relatives and friends who gathered around the fireplace on the long winter nights telling their stories—all true, even the made up parts. Aunt Zella and Uncle Hall will always stand above all the rest. My mother told her stories in songs from ballads of the old country seasoned with songs of what I think of now as the great depression, hobos, and the Birmingham Jail.

I owe heartfelt thanks to so many talented teachers, so many there's no way to name them all. In high school literature class, petite Miss Mary Cannon spun romantic tales of her secret lover, Sir Walter Scott. Later when I saw Scotland's moss covered castles, heather covered hills and walked by the sparkling streams and lakes, I felt like I'd been there before with the first Ellen, the *Lady of the Lake*.

Over mugs of honey mead, stern but funny Dr. Virginia Smith at Bethel College (now Bethel University) introduced me to the epic Beowulf who fights the monster Grendel, Grendel's mother, and a fire breathing dragon. In a dimly lit cold dank beer hall her voice echoed and rattled across the chasm of the ages. I sat shivering filled with awe watching the monsters fight in the shadows. Sometime before morning light after many mugs of mead, we passed out and slept the rest of the night on the cold stone floor.

"Stories and myths," writes Karen Armstrong in *A Short History of Myth*, "reflect and shape our lives. They explore our narratives that remind us of what it means to be human."

I owe Ellen, my favorite teacher and my mate for 63 short years, more than I can even talk about. She has saved my life and our marriage more times than once. How many miles do you suppose we've walked at night on the rails and country roads? And if this work should ever see the light of day, I must again express sincere appreciation to El for showing me the way.

Thanks to Dariel Mayer of Periploi Press for her careful editing, artistic design, and most of all, her grace and patience.

A while back I read a *Time* essay by Roger Rosenblatt entitled "Why Do We Write." He recounts stories of doomed people who used their last precious moments to write. Lt. Captain Dmitri Kolesnikov's dying message to his wife from the sunken submarine Kursk is one example. What Kolesnikov did others have also done. When a JAL airliner went down in 1985, passengers used long minutes of its terrible spiraling descent to write letters to loved ones. When the last occupants of the Warsaw Ghetto had finally seen their families and companions die of disease and starvation or watched them carried off in trucks to extermination camps and there could be no doubt of their own fate, they took scraps of paper on which they wrote poems, thoughts, fragments of their lives, rolled them into tight scrolls and slipped them into the crevices of the ghetto walls.

A number of years ago Jean-Dominique Bauby, the editor of *Elle* magazine in Paris, was felled by a stroke so destructive that the only part of his body that could move was his left eyelid. Flicking that eyelid he managed to signal the letters of the alphabet and proceeded to write his autobiography, *The Diving Bell and the Butterfly*, the last grand gesture of his life.

Imagine yourself sitting in total darkness drawing your last breaths calling to a comrade, "I am here," as if to confirm I am … and then you write your words to leave your record. I remember similar moments during World War II in a dark London subway writing in my journal as German rockets and firebombs fell. In combat and in the hospitals I've seen soldiers writing short notes or long letters to family and loved ones. "Mail this if I don't make it."

Life is a mystery. Words are a mystery. I've written poems about words. Nothing more than mysterious marks and scratches on scrolls or paper. Words about other words, but somehow when properly pieced together, making enough sense to let another know how you think or feel.

PROSE

An Introduction

Stephen Allen Freeland

This is the kind of day poets would like to hold in their minds and write about; the air is cool and crisp, the landscape painted in all the colors and mystery of early fall, and the road winding itself from Camden to Big Sandy through cut-over woods, harvested fields and gardens, and homes all coming alive for another day.

Pete and Butch are probably delivering the *Magic Valley Times* by now. This thought reminds me that I must still distribute papers to Bruceton, Huntingdon and McKenzie. I silently curse the paper for this job and again twofold for the challenge before me. Damn.

Dad and I are on our way to Big Sandy High School to instruct a workshop on radio and newspaper communication if you can believe that. We'll meet the *Times* editor, Charles Farmer, at the library for the class.

Mike Freeland, my father, will be in charge of speech instruction. Charles will teach writing. I'm along to glow in the starlight.

As our jeep tops the last hills and curves, Dad thinks aloud, "I really don't know what's going to happen. Mr. Knight told me he's going to have everyone from the seventh grade on, but I asked him to limit it to only those seriously interested in writing or speaking. Maybe we won't have more than a dozen or so, that's a bunch of kids. Just keep your fingers crossed."

Dad parks the jeep in front of the sign that reads "School Bus Parking Only." We pause for a moment, and then walk toward the school.

In spite of myself I'm starting to feel a rush of excitement although I've been through this drill before. I'm on to Dad's tricks and I'm pretty sure that he knows that I know. So rather than tell me, "Come with me. You might learn something," he pretends I'm needed to run the recorder and distribute handouts.

I look at my father walking ahead of me in his serious gray flannel three button business suit, white shirt, contrasting rust colored tie with its careful Windsor knot, a briefcase in each hand but I imagine him in pressed military uniform wearing his polished paratrooper boots with combat gear in the big war he never talks about. I see a middle-age stranger, growing bald and thick at the waist. I wonder what he's like in his private world especially on the long solitary walks at night or those days when he disappears to the farm with the dogs. Am I seeing a glimpse of myself when I'm his age. For a moment, sadness sweeps over me with the sudden realization that we've never once had an honest from the heart conversation, not one. Not just me, either. I don't think he's ever talked to my brothers, maybe Patricia but when we do talk some, we might as well be on stage, self consciously reading lines from a script. I can't explain it because in front of an audience or a class, he becomes another person relaxed, loose, having fun. He kind of forgets himself when he's on his feet working but not working he's a recluse and a hermit.

Standing in the doorway of the library is Mr. James Knight the school principal who had promised to cut the number of those attending. The tall broad-shouldered former coach stands there as though unsure of whether we should go in. On his face there is a shy, sheepish grin, the kind you smile when you are caught in a school boy prank.

He greets us and waves us in. Packed into that small library are at least 200 grinning students who look as though they might all be shyster lawyers ready to challenge anyone who might have the audacity to face them down.

Over at the other end of the room Charles Farmer leans against one of the desks.

The room settles down and gradually becomes quiet.

Dad carefully places his books, hand-outs and two trophies on a table and stands before the students. He waits—silent for long moments before speaking . . . "Do you know who you are?" he asks. "You are a *miracle*—a marvel, unique. In the millions of years that have passed there has never been another person like you. And never will be. You want to learn to write? Speak? *You can do it!* It's up to you."

Soon he directs volunteers to the front of the class to introduce themselves, "Tell us who you are . . . why are you here?"

To my surprise, the students shy at first, start talking:

"I'm going to be a teacher."

"A lawyer."

"I'll witness for Jesus—nothing would make me happier."

"I hope what we learn today will help me make better grades."

And between comments and answering questions, they hear again affirmations—*you are special.* You have greatness within you.

Follow your dream. You can do it. Believe in yourself. Remember to be your own best friend.

When we divide into small groups, I join Charles Farmer's class on creative writing and how to write the basic news story.

Charles says, "I want you to learn how to express yourself with a pen. For me, there's nothing more satisfying. Think of it: you make these strange marks on paper; someone else looks at it and can tell what you're thinking about. It's like magic or mystery. *Words are your tools* learn and become familiar with as many as you can. The more words you have in your tool box, the more successful you'll be. That's a fact. But," he cautioned, "never use a big word when a small word will do just as well. Your job is to be *understood* . . . not to impress someone with big words that you know."

At the end of the day, Mr. Knight, with a grin on his face, an I-told-you-so look in his eyes, asks for brief oral or written reports:

. . . "I wish there'd been more time."

. . . "I was just getting started."

Kathy Hartsfield, "I'll be more careful and conscious about what I say."

"I'll use these skills when I get to college," Katrina Davis.

"Mr. Farmer says we can get out our own school paper."

One of the quieter students sitting by the door said, "I'm going to work for a radio station."

"My wife told me this would be awful—a lot of bored kids who don't care about anything, but I've never seen a more enthusiastic bunch." Was Charles Farmer's reaction.

Mr. Knight's response, "I don't think I've ever seen a rowdier bunch having more fun, or learning more . . . more than I expected."

And I expect I'll remember this workshop as fun as well, revealing and instructive for the students and faculty and Dad and Charles and me (even).

That evening as the sun was sinking behind the hills and trees of the Magic Valley giving its final luminous rays of light to a day that had passed much too soon, I praised my providence that I'm allowed to deliver the newspaper one more time. My star shineth.

To Teach To Love

Michael Freeland

Notes from the Big Sandy High School Workshop and many others over these forty years and counting: You are a miracle, you are unique. I quote Pablo Casals and use this familiar handout with almost every class:

> When will we teach our children in school what they are? We should say to each of them: Do you know what you are? You are a marvel. You are unique. In all of the world there is no other child like you. In the millions of years that have passed there has never been another child like you. And look at your body—what a wonder it is! Your legs, your arms, your cunning fingers, the way you move! You may become a Shakespeare, a Michelangelo, a Beethoven. You have the capacity for anything. Yes, you are a marvel. And when you grow up, can you then harm another who is, like you, a marvel?
> —*Pablo Casals, from* Joys and Sorrows, *Simon & Schuster, 1970*

To the students, I say look *where* you are. Today we have gathered on ancient sacred grounds . . . when the last great ice age still held the world in its frozen grasp, many of our ancestors first gazed upon these green valleys of the Tennessee River. Ancient people lived here where you now live about 5200 BC. If that's not special I say, you could fool me. Look it up. (*Tribes That Slumber,* Lewis and Kneberg)

I tell the students, "So help me to understand. You are God like, or God within you, walking on trails 5,200 years old. Think about that. Straighten your shoulders. Look people in the eye. Be confident."

We break into small discussion groups using my poem *Once* as a guide.

> Once my brothers, ancient scribes and
> Herdsmen gazed at a star-filled sky
> With wonder even as I do now.
> Who am I?
> Why am I?
> Am I?

Steve says I use this exercise with every group, even kindergartners, which of course is almost true.

When I'm on a roll, I say, "If you're really serious about writing—and life—keep a journal. You don't have to write every day, but most days, even if your entry is little more than the weather, a note to yourself or a poem. Today for example think of National Poetry Month, a glorious day of fresh colors, soft wind and sunshine. Write a poem for God's sake (yes, for God's sake), and give it to someone you love. Plant a tree and name it for someone. Take a long walk alone, or better, with your dog. Walk a new way, not the usual path through the woods but cut across the fields. Every day read something serious that causes you to think. Have you read *Anna Karenina?* I haven't either, but it's on my list.

"Most Important: Remember, no one is coming. Write this in your journal. *Your success and education is up to you.* The most important thing I learned in my modest country high school was self-education. Once you realize learning is up to you, you have the right attitude to succeed in school and beyond."

I confess to this big problem when I'm writing—I'm trying to create and critique at the same time. It can't be done, like trying to get hot and cold water from the same faucet at the same time. At the present moment, for example, the right side of my brain is creatively pushing out words while, at the same time, the left side of my brain is busy attacking, analyzing, trying to kill every thought.

I ought to try harder to heed the advice I preach, write because you must—or for the sheer joy of it. Write to cure the itch—through your pain, joy, surprise and whatever else is holding you back. Write to keep your sanity. Write only the stark, naked truth as though nobody else will ever read it. Write for yourself but with confidence. Push through all of your self-doubts and simply tell your story. This much I guarantee, everyone has a story to tell and yours needs to be told. No one else in this whole wide world can tell your story as well as you can.

When you write and speak, tell the truth; this advice goes back to the early Greeks and Romans. All good writers speak in honest voices. Asked what makes students write badly, Eudora Welty once said the trouble with bad student writing is the trouble with all bad writing. It is not serious and it does not tell the truth.

In the book, *Writing to Be Read*, Macrorie makes a connection between the things written about, the words used in the writing, and your real experience in the world you know well—whether in fact or dream or imagination, the message: Keep it real.

A few weeks ago Dianne Bucy gave a reading in class from her work, "My Hero." This is an example of from-the-gut honest writing, as good as anything I've ever read:

> I don't know why I never refer to my daddy as my hero. Anyone
> who knows me knows he was. Maybe it's because I grew up
> in a time heroes were larger-than-life and usually had super-
> human powers. My daddy was so real and down-to-earth. He
> was a simple man with only a fifth grade education, but in no
> way was he simple in mind. He could judge a person's character
> in one meeting and I never knew him to be wrong. He wasn't a

perfect man. My mama said the day he found the Lord he had whiskey on his breath.

This is honest writing. I'll follow this writer wherever she wants to go. The poet Will Stafford said: "When you write, simply tell me something." You'll notice that Diane didn't try to impress by using big words.

Your job is to be understood, not to show off your impressive vocabulary. If you reach for highfaluting language, it can backfire. Readers could think you're being pompous or fake as a three dollar bill.

In *The Miracle of Language,* Richard Lederer writes: "Use small, old words where you can. If a long word says just what you want to say, do not fear to use it. But know that our tongue is rich in crisp, brisk, swift, short words. Make them the spine and the heart of what you speak and write. Short words are like fast friends. They will not let you down."

Be careful to make every word pull its own weight. Less is more, as a general rule. When you can chop off a word or paragraph, what you'll find left behind is more clear, concise, and valuable—even beautiful.

Matthew May, in *In Pursuit of Elegance* tells us "A great piece of art is composed not just of what is in the final piece, but equally what is not. It is the discipline to discard what does not fit—to cut out what might have already cost days or even years of effort—that distinguishes the truly exceptional artists and marks the ideal piece of work, be it a symphony, a novel, a painting, a company, or most important of all, a life."

Say in a few words all you want to say with precision and fullness. You will please yourself and your readers. We all love people who say a great deal in a few words. Most of us feel that life is too short; so we praise a person who can hammer the nail with three blows.

My mantra has remained the same as yesterday: Everybody has a story to tell. Told in your own unique voice all made up of words, rhythms, thoughts, visions, pain, love, hope, experiences that come to us in different ways from an unrepeatable life. Write as if there's no tomorrow.

When you write, pull the reader into your present moment with the power of *now*. To convince your reader that she is with you, assault each of her senses in turn with color, sound, taste, and texture. Allow your reader to walk with you through the colorful theater of the mind. Let her feel the pale slanting sun, hear the wind rattling leaves in the trees, smell the saddle leather and the coming rain. Let your companion (the reader) feel what you're sensing at the moment: joy, pain, frustration, homesickness. Let her stand with you in the middle of it all.

I'll not remember what you said or how you said it but I'll always remember how you made me feel.

Your development as a writer is not the knowledge of this or that grammatical point or style but to simply sit down and write and then rewrite. It was Hemingway who said genius is found by about the seventh draft. First drafts won't cut it.

For one of the most important lessons I've learned, I return to the year 1973, my first year as a rookie part-time professor at the University of Tennessee, Martin. In my interview for the job I was asked to write about a page entitled "My Backyard." I thought the guy was kidding. "What?" "Just write," he said.

I recall something I wrote about our yard in McKenzie, just three lines:

> The back part was once a CCC (Civilian Conservation Corps) training ground. Looking west I can see railroad tracks and some trees and a few patches of hollyhocks in bloom near the barn out back.

That was about it. His eminence, the dean, glanced at my paper and tossed it back to me, "Our freshmen write better."

Then he handed me this paper, "Take a look at this. See what you can learn about *specifics* and *feelings* from Larry Barnett. Larry is one of our freshmen."

The paper read:

I walk into the middle of the yard and lie down on the grass. It is dead and brown with the feel of a stiff brush. Closing my eyes I can hear the rushing of the wind. It hums in the wires of the television antenna, and with its breath allows each tree and bush the opportunity to sing its own song. This is not a wind that lives here. It is a traveling wind in a hurry and only passing through. With it the wind carries a sound like an approaching car heard far down a hilly, country road.

Opening my eyes, I look to my left where the overturned garden smelling of moist cotton hulls and wild onions lies. Along the left perimeter there are pine trees. These are the live part of the yard at this time of year . . . sighing and singing the yard to winter sleep as they sway in the wind. . . .

I lie back and stare at the cloudless, perfect sky . . . a rich blue liquid that runs down the air to the horizon . . . the kind of sky that makes me search its face for some flaw. The sun is warm and bright and pours over the yard like honey, dripping from its every feature . . .

You will notice this student's essay has feeling—like a stiff brush—the sun warm—the yard sings its own song—the rushing of the wind—the smell of wild onions—moist earth and cold air. There's more of course but you get the idea.

Now consider this example:

Once on a cold November day, in the middle of a red clay
cotton field, cold drizzle splashed on my face as I lifted my
aching shoulders and surveyed the world I knew. My eyes
fell on a father frustrated in his efforts to provide the good
life for the woman he loved and the children she bore him. I
looked to the endless cotton row, to the horizon hemmed by
the day's gray clouds and I looked down at the red mud at my
feet. I looked at my scarred hands—my torn cuticles ached—
my fingers were black and cold. I felt the prick of the bolls
and I wondered who am I?
  —*"Secret of Once," Ellen Freeland*

This paragraph has character and soul. Most important, it re-
veals the soul of an honest writer and demonstrates some of the
things we've been talking about. You're standing with the writer in
the middle of a red clay cotton field—*presence,* you *feel* your aching
shoulders, the cold drizzle on your face, you *see* the endless cotton
row . . . the aloneness and you are left with a sense of wonder—
wanting more.

Another example:

March 3, 2010, Port au Prince, Haiti.
I walk from the plane along the corridor to the street. Black
faces are all around me, separated from me by a chain link
fence, fingers clutching the links, black eyes watch as I pass by.
Serious, desperate, sad. Why do I come to the place they would
love to leave?
  The hospital is not far away. We pass through the city
to get there. I think it is a sunny day but this whole world is
black. Devastation is everywhere. Buildings are toppled, collapsed, leaning precariously. Bewildered faces stare at the
destruction. People aimlessly collect rubble in wheelbarrows:
a seemingly hopeless task. Dead bodies are lying in the street,

under cars, crushed by collapsed buildings. Thousands of tents in every available space, crowded, piled on top of one another. Children play among the rubble; dead bodies litter this devil's playground.

I reach the hospital where I will work. It is an old hospital now turned over to victims of the earthquake. The hospital is packed with the living and the dying. Huge dark rooms make up the wards, each packed with patients. Beds are so close that you can barely pass between them, each filled with a broken black body. Black eyes look at me in pain, desperation, sadness, fear . . . hope. Almost everyone has a broken bone, a missing part, old, young, male, female.

The Haitian doctor takes me from bed to bed presenting overwhelming problems. They speak French, I English. We cannot communicate in words but we communicate. My brain is on overload; where do I begin? How can I fix this? Clashing thoughts bounce around in my head. What am I doing here? Why did I not come sooner? I want the safety of my home. How can I stay longer? Routine begins without fanfare. I operate all day; seeing ward and clinic patients between surgeries.

The operating rooms are small and dark. Much of the equipment is obsolete, but the hardware—plates and screws I use—is state of the art, provided by medical supply companies from around the world. We work from dawn to dusk, fixing bones, amputating limbs, draining abscesses.

We then walk from the hospital to our compound where we eat and sleep. After dinner we walk back to the hospital where the staff will socialize with the patients. I carry my guitar in hand. Our flashlight cuts a narrow path through the blackness. But the blackness knows that in the end it will win. The patients have all gathered in one ward. Some are in wheelchairs, some on crutches, others on stretchers. They fill the beds, every chair, the floor. We are shoulder to shoulder, one large breathing organism in this dark room.

And then they sing.

From these black faces come incredibly beautiful sounds, filling the black room, spilling out into blackness. They sing of a loving and caring God and I wonder, "Where is this God?" The voices are full of love and hope. I think, "How can this be?" These broken and hurt people who have lost everything—family, home, limbs, jobs, sing of hope and love and the goodness of their God. How can this be? In this black room I am amazed, bewildered, elated . . . angered. They sing *Amazing Grace,* a song written by an English slave trader who probably carried some of their ancestors in a ship of unimaginable squalor and pain, stripping them of their dignity and freedom, to this island where their children now find more squalor, pain, indignity. Even the selection of their songs seems inappropriate. And yet, this scene is one of the most impressive I have ever experienced.

And so our time goes. Spending each day working through a sea of broken people. Fixing some; unable to fix others. And all too soon it is time to leave. And I don't want to go.

The color black is the absorption of all the colors of the spectrum. Out of this blackness I have seen the brightness of the unflagging human spirit. I have seen joy in the face of despair; hope in the face of devastation. I have taken away from this place more than I have given. And part of my soul is still there in that black place with them.

—*"Fade to Black,"* Gene Gulish, M. D.

Again, remember what the poet said, "Be serious and tell the truth." This is the truth, plain, simple, unadorned—serious writing for a purpose.

The Spring of '43

Gene Gulish

The gentle late April breeze blew the white lace curtains through the open window into the bedroom. The morning spring sun filled the room with golden light.

The boy woke and stretched. He sat up in the bed. "Grandmother," he said to the form lying next to him, "It is time to get up." "I will rest for a few more minutes," she replied.

"You go downstairs and play. I will be there soon." The boy tumbled out of bed. He was wearing only undershorts, "gotches" she called them. He walked down the hall of this big old brick farmhouse. All of the other bedrooms were empty. He ran down the stairs into the living room of the old house—his house—the only house that he had ever known. He climbed into the big overstuffed chair and leafed through some of his children's books. This chair was his favorite place in the whole house. Most of their days would end here. His grandmother would sit in the chair. He would climb into her lap. She would fold him into her strong arms and they would talk or sing or just sit quietly. They were both bilingual, speaking Hungarian and English. Most of the time when they were together they spoke Hungarian or a mixture of Hungarian and English.

Sometimes she would tell him of her life in the Old Country—Hungary. She talked about how her husband John and she came to America. John was a coal miner and then a farmer. He had never seen John. John had died many years ago. She talked of raising her 10 children, one of whom was his father, in this house. Sometimes they would sing: "You are my sunshine, my only sunshine, you make me happy when skies are gray, you'll never know dear, how much I love you, please don't take my sunshine away."

Sometimes he would wrap his arms around her neck, feeling pure unconditional love, even before he could verbalize it. He never wondered why he was here and not with his parents. This was his whole world. Often he would fall asleep in her lap and find himself the next morning in their bed. Sometimes he would ask, "Grandmother, will we always live here when I grow up?" She would smile and say, "I will see you start school, but I will not see you finish it." He never understood what that meant. He was 5—5 ½ if you asked him, and he would be in the first grade in the fall.

He jumped out of the chair and ran to the stairs, "Wake up Grandmother" he called,"I'm hungry."

"I'm coming." She moved slowly down the stairs and made it to the chair and fell into it. She moaned softly. Her long black and gray hair fell over her shoulders. She whispered his name, barely audibly. And then her head fell backward against the back of the chair; then silence. He stood frozen in front of her. His lower lip quivered. "Don't cry little man," she would say—sometimes lovingly when he had fallen down and skinned his knee, sometimes sternly when he was using tears to get what he wanted. He did not cry. Her hand slipped off the arm of the chair. He reached over and put it back.

He knew of death. She talked about his grandfather dying. Sometimes she would wring the neck of a chicken which they would then have for Sunday dinner. Once his father and some men had come over and shot a pig and then cut its throat. But death could not happen to her. She must be asleep. "It is okay Grandmother," he said. "You rest and I will get dressed." He slipped into his jeans and shirt. Then he sat in front of her and demonstrated his new learned skill—tying his shoe laces. He made himself a bowl of cold cereal for breakfast. "You stay there, Grandmother, I will go out and feed the chickens." He did this. Then he gathered the hen's eggs, dropping only one as he made his way back to the house. "I fed the chickens and gathered the eggs," he said. "I dropped only one."

No answer. Silence. After awhile he went outside and sat on the back step of the house. His beagle dog came up immediately and sat beside him. "Grandmother is still sleeping," he said to the dog.

Beside the step the red and yellow tulips were in bloom. He remembered last fall when they were planting them in the cold. He was complaining about his hands being cold. She said, "Never mind. You will enjoy the flowers in the spring." He looked at them now. They were very pretty.

After awhile he decided to walk to the woods at the back of their farm—a privilege he had only recently been granted—to go there alone. He loved the forest. A squirrel chattered at him from an overhead branch. Birds were everywhere. The forest floor was a carpet of wild flowers. He gathered a few to take them back to his Grandmother when she awoke. When he entered the house, its silence frightened him. He checked on his Grandmother. She had not moved. "I brought you some flowers," he said, knowing now that she would not answer. The day passed. As the sun traveled west, clouds began to gather. After awhile he returned to the living room. Her hand had again fallen off the arm of the chair. He went over and replaced it. Her hand was cold! He sat on the floor in front of her. He wrapped his skinny arms around his skinny legs, resting his chin on his bony knees. He sat in silence. The clouds outside filled the room with gloom. A gentle rain began to fall.

He felt a tear make its way down his cheek. Then another, and another. "Don't cry little man," he heard her say in his head. He buried his face into his knees. Sobbing turned into the wail of a mortally wounded animal. Outside the rain beat against the window pane, "Let me in to share your agony." The thunder roared his grief. The lightening mirrored his sorrow. After a while he stopped crying. He got up. In the failing light of the house, he made his way up the stairs to their bedroom. He took his pillow off the bed and headed to the stairs. He stopped and returned to the bedroom. He returned his pillow and took hers. He could smell her on it. Clutching it gave him solace. He returned to the chair. He placed the pillow at her feet. Pulling a blanket off the couch, he covered himself, and curled up in a ball. He was instantly asleep.

And that is where they found him the next morning.
Asleep at the feet of his dead grandmother.
Asleep at the feet of his dead world.
That is where they found him.

School Bells

Larry T. McGehee, 1936–2008,
Henry County native, educator, essayist, lecturer

My mother couldn't wait until December to give me my present—a Christmas bell.

This is no ordinary bell, but a brass hand bell that belonged to my late Aunt Charlie, principal from 1922 to 1955 of the Robert E. Lee Elementary School that my mother, her brother and sisters, my cousins and my brother and I all attended, and across the street from our home where the family lived for the six or so best years of my life.

Aunt Charlie, or "Miss Charlie" as generations of schoolchildren remember her, had joined the school faculty there in 1909. When she was forced by age laws to retire forty-six years later, she went back to college to upgrade her teaching certificate by taking some physical education courses, lied about her age, and was hired to teach in Florida, where she taught another five or so years before returning to our family center in Paris, Tennessee.

Her students recall her mostly for her discipline. She used the big brass bell to start and end the school day and to call each class in from recess, but she didn't need it. More often she simply clapped her hands. Her former students liken that sound to a crack of thunder. She commanded instant attention and respect from every student she supervised. In her retirement in her eighties, she attended a dinner across town, to which she walked. She had never learned to drive, and she preferred not to waste her scant teachers' retirement money on a taxi. It was dark when the dinner was over, and a middle-aged former student, recalling the manners she drilled into him, offered to walk her home. She refused his offer, saying she was unafraid to go alone because, "I can lick any man in this town—and have."

Her middle name was Irene, but no one ever used that. The Charlie allegedly came from a relative who died young. Through her career, she left behind more children she called her own than any other spinster I have ever heard of.

She was actually my great-aunt, one of my grandfather's four sisters, all of whom where schoolteachers. They were all well-educated and well-read. Granddaddy himself had not gone to school, although he was as good at reading and figuring as anyone I have ever known. After thirty years delivering rural mail, he devoted thirty-three years of his own retirement to politics, served on school boards, got a high school built in his district, got roads connecting the county schools built, and pushed hard for an education agenda all his life.

So Aunt Charlie's school bell has within it a lot of family tradition in the good cause of education. I have always lusted after the bell for what it symbolizes and have tried to lead my own life in continuity with the service to education those great-aunts and their brother bequeathed to me. Next year will mark my own half-century of being in schoolhouses. I know I am here in faithfulness to the family fixation with education, but I've never had the temptation to leave; there's too much left to do and to learn to ever think of not being an educator.

Aunt Charlie used to say she never had a bad student, and I've claimed to have never had a bad teacher. We probably have both been naïve and utopian about how important education is and about the prospects for making and keeping education's institutions good, but in a world where good causes go begging, she chose one of the best ones to champion. By giving me her great cause to fight, she gave me the greatest gift of all. She was truly a very great great-aunt.

Getting her bell is icing on the cake. It passed upon her death to her youngest sister, and from her to her son, and thence to the son's widow, whose own children unselfishly agreed that I should have it. After several unbroken decades of getting pajamas and shirts from Mother for Christmas, she has at last located a perfect gift. It more than makes up for not getting an electric train years ago.

The bell will rest conspicuously in a glass dome on a walnut base with a brass plaque as long as I am still around. To my absolute delight, our daughters have already begun to lay claims for who will get it after that. It pleases me that they have developed such keen eyes for things of true value. I suspect they got some of that from a great, great Aunt Charlie they never knew

The School Bus

Chris Evans, Editor/Publisher
The Crittenden Press, Marion, Kentucky

Children simply adore "old yeller" and I don't mean the dog. Bus 18 was the cheese wagon I boarded as a child. Much like my own younguns, brother and I got on the bus early, sometimes before daylight until the time changed. That's one of the perils of living way out in the country. When the school bus turns around in your driveway and heads back toward town, you know you're at the end of the line and it's going to be a long ride.

The school bus is an education in and of itself. I would almost bet that more of life's lessons are presented in back seats of a bus than in a traditional classroom.

My brood loves the bus. Tried to get the boy to ride with me to school one day last week. Threw in a free breakfast, but he turned it down. Cried to be able to stay on schedule and ride the bus to school.

They think the world of their driver, too. It's Houston Peek. My 10-year-old daughter announced after school started this year that her kindergarten brother was told by the driver to sit close to the front. Didn't ask why, but it's pretty apparent based on recollections from my own childhood.

The back of the bus was for older kids. Front was for pups. It was, and still is, a linear hierarchy. That was an unwritten rule. Pass the midway point and you were apt to get your ear thumped or worse yet, burned by some four-letter words that an elementary student shouldn't know.

A child's vocabulary is always increased once he or she graduates to the rear of the bus. Thirty-five years ago an older girl introduced me to some terms for which I had no prior knowledge. They were words that for one reason or another we tend to learn, use during adolescence out of the hearing of adults, then try to impress friends with later in high school and college. After that, we find that society really frowns upon the use of such verbal expression and our poison tongues are muted until we smash our thumb with a hammer or break a bolt off in the oil pan.

The spit wad, knuckle thumping and thumb wars were prevalent in the back of the bus. A spit wad is a rather disgusting thing if you stop and think about it, especially if it's a fresh one. We thumped knuckles to see who was the toughest. A little blood meant you were a real warrior. Thumb wars were similar, yet for the more refined bus rider. There was never any sign of blood during such activity, but tempers could flare resulting in an elbow being thrown.

"Sarge" is what we called our bus driver. He lived right down the road from the parents and grandparents and had known the family for three generations. Anything I did on the bus quickly made its way home because the grandparents ran a general store and the bus driver always stopped in for a cold drink after the morning route.

Freeze out was the most popular event on the bus. In the dead of winter we'd drop all of the windows and see who was the first to give. Almost always, "Sarge" intervened and stopped the game before anyone's lips turned blue.

Smoking on the bus was the cardinal sin. Sarge must have had eyes in the back of his head—to go along with that long thin mirror above his seat—because rarely did someone hotbox a stogie and get away with it. The penalty was being kicked off the bus. For kids in my neighborhood that was akin to the death penalty. We lived a long way from town and back then most families had just one car. That complicated transportation logistics if you were banned from the bus.

One lady I know calls the school bus the Golden Angel that comes to pick up her children and give her respite for the day. It's like a big yellow valium. Another refers to the bus as the Cootie Coach. Not sure why.

Have things changed over the years? Do our children endure the same trials and tribulations we did on old yeller? Sure they do. Bus drivers may come and go, but the things kids do and learn on the cheese wagon are timeless.

Come with Me

Douglas Lee Freeland

I think of those long ago summers as one special summer—an innocent time without cell phones, personal computers or 24-hour cable TV. Through the soft lens of my memory I hear Buffalo calling, "Doub? Whoa Doub, where you at? "In another life Buff must have been a drill sergeant but a sergeant with a sense of humor and a sweet personality.

Buffalo was Mr. Willie Ralston, an ancient black man who didn't live far from our home on Paris Avenue. Buff lived in a small house behind the Church of Christ just off Highland Drive. I'm not sure how he got the nickname Buffalo but I'm sure he earned it. His story is well known. He worked for the H. C. Spinks Clay Company during World War II and was involved in a construction accident when he was run over by a bulldozer, breaking, according to legend, every bone in his body. After spending several weeks in the hospital, he was back to work, people say, stronger than ever. Buff stood 5'7", stout as a mule with Popeye arms that could swing an ax, briar hook or sledge hammer better than John Henry the steel driving man.

Our yard was known around town for having some of the biggest and most productive pecan trees this side of Georgia. In the fall neighbors would come over and pick up pecans to be used in making pecan pies. When a couple of trees in the yard developed worm infestation, Dad was worried the disease would spread to the other trees in the yard, so he had them cut down. Buffalo, Boy Blue, and some other men brought chain saws to the yard and cut down the trees. "Mister Mike?" Buffalo asked. "You want me to bring a tractor or a dozer to get up them stumps?"

Dad grinned, "No, Buffalo. I have a better idea. Doug, *come with me*." I spent the next few weeks with my brother David digging out those stumps. Pecan trees have really long tap roots reaching almost all the way to China. For long hours in the early morning and the evening, we dug around the big stumps. Two or three feet out from the side of the stump, I'd go after the tap root with a pry bar. It took a few days but we—Buff, David, and I—eventually got the stump up. Victory. I looked over at Buff. He grinned and pointed to the next stump a few feet away.

"Might s'well get started on das one, Doub. Hit ain't gonna get up by hisself."

"Come with me" started every morning at 8 o'clock sharp, rain or shine. Dad never ran out of jobs whether digging up stumps, clearing out overgrown fence rows, or putting up new fences. There was always plenty of work to be done around the yard or on the farm up at Buchanan.

"Doub, you and Davis ready to work?"

"Yes, Sir."

David is three years younger than I and hated being called the baby of the family. But he was a hard worker always eager to please. David's a charmer, laid back. "He could talk the socks off a billy goat." Neighbors on Paris Avenue thought he was a little angel. Mrs. Alta Connell told Mom, "David is such a sweet little boy." The whole time I knew he was planning adventures and hijinks for the night. He'd tell our parents good night, and then go downstairs to his bedroom with his dog Richard, turn off the lights and pretend to go to sleep. After a little while, he'd slip out of bed and out the window of his bedroom and go who knows where. One night after an evening at the Dairy Queen or cruising town in his jeep, he came back slipping in a little after midnight, carefully raising his bedroom window, he swung one leg over the sill. Just as he was about to duck his head under the window, there was a tap on his shoulder. Dad had been standing in the shadows waiting—tomorrow will be another long day at the farm, another day to remember "Come with me."

Lunch break at the farm meant riding with Buffalo in his old white GMC pickup with the dogs to Clayton's Store for white bread sandwiches filled with thick slices of bologna and mayonnaise or cheese and crackers washed down with Coca Cola.

"How long we working today?" I asked Buff.

"From can to can't. We gots lots to do this day. Ain't no time like now to get started." With that, lunch was over and we were back to cleaning out the hedgerow.

When Buff swung an ax or a briar hook, he would grunt—not really as much a grunt as a statement. "Hah!" he would go as his powerful blow struck the base of a briar bush. "Hah!" another blow. "Ah right!" he would go as he hit another stroke. Then just like that the sapling would be down. "Doub, take this big branch then stack the smaller ones on top an' you can pull the whole pile out to the brush pile by tote'n that one large limb." This is a technique I use to this day when I'm working in the yard. Stack smaller limbs on larger limbs and drag the whole pile out to the street. Back then we would stack the limbs and branches into the back of Buff's truck and he would haul them to the dump or take them somewhere and burn them.

In the summer after my junior year in high school Dad purchased a farm not far from WKTA-FM on the Huntingdon highway. The farm had low lying land down by the railroad tracks that ran into McKenzie. Buff, David, and I were to build a fence around that acreage. The lower end of the farm was the closest thing to a swamp I've ever seen and stayed wet most of the summer. Perfect breeding ground for some of the biggest mosquitoes I ever saw. A shallow ditch ran from north to south cutting through the middle of the field.

Cleaning out thickets and fence rows became our specialty. If colleges gave credit for fence row cleaning, we'd all have Ph.D's. Thickets were heavy with small black oak saplings, wild cherry bushes, saw briars, honeysuckle, poison ivy, and fat copperhead snakes. Poison ivy is a curse. Scratch on it and it spreads all over your body.

The fence we built that summer was a metal post fence with corner posts made from old utility poles sunk about 3 to 4 feet deep and anchored with concrete. Those anchors were placed at the corners and every couple of hundred feet in straight rows, and used as anchor posts for stretching the wire. Each anchor post consisted of two, and at a corner, three posts with a creosote soaked pole placed diagonally from top to bottom between the posts for support.

We rolled the wire fencing out from one set of posts to the next and attached the fencing to the first set of corner posts using steel fence staples. When the fence was in the right spot, we took a contraption that looked like some sort of medieval torture device and clamped it onto the fence at the next anchor post. The clamp consisted of two, two by fours that were bolted to opposite sides of the fence. Attached to each end of the two x fours was a chain that had a long logging chain fastened to its middle. Another chain with a double clawed device was fastened to the other anchor post. The two claws had pivot points then we used a pry bar to walk the claws up the chain thus stretching the fence.

When summer first started, it took David and me working together to get the fence fully stretched. By the end of summer I was able to fully stretch the wire by myself. We guessed that by the time we got the fencing fully stretched out there had to be at least 500 pounds of pressure on the chains and the person working the fulcrum. Stretching the fence that summer turned out to be my summer conditioning and strength training for football my senior year. Once the fence was stretched into place, we used steel fence staples to attach it to the anchor posts.

We drove the metal fence posts into the ground every ten to twelve feet between the anchor post using the five pound-hammer that Buff had. David would hold the post until I got it started. It was a dangerous job and my aim wasn't very good. I don't remember ever mashing his finger but I came close a few times. Finally he got too gun-shy to hold the post for me and I had to learn how to hold the post with one hand and get it started by holding the hammer close to the head and tapping it the first few inches into the ground. Up on the hill that was a bit of a challenge because the ground was dry and hard; down at the bottom of the hill in the wet marshy area, it wasn't nearly as hard. The fence posts were placed on the outside of the wire fencing and attached from the back side to the posts using metal clips. This was done to prevent cattle, or other livestock, from pushing the fence away from the post and breaking the fence down.

One day after lunch Buffalo was supposed to stop by the lumber yard and pick up some creosote posts for bracing and some sand, rocks and cement to mix the concrete to anchor the posts. He had the back end of that beat up old GMC pickup truck so loaded down that the springs were fully compressed and the bed of the truck was down on the tires. Buff had watched me pull posts down to the bottom of the field for weeks and decided, "if that ol' zeep can pull them posts through the mud, I can pull my truck through too." He obviously had forgotten that he was loaded with concrete material and posts. Now mind you, that ditch really wasn't more than a low spot in the field but between the load and the fact that his truck a two-wheel-drive, he had no business trying to drive it through there. David and I looked up and saw him trying to come across the field. We just looked at each other and broke out laughing. Sure enough he got stuck trying to cross the ditch.

There he sat in the driver's seat of the truck, rear end buried up to the axles in mud, tires spinning with no traction. David and I went over to the driver's window and told him to hold up. I would get the Jeep and attach a chain to the front frame of his truck. With the truck loaded to the gills we still didn't have traction to pull it out. We placed a piece of tin roofing on the ground (Buff always had stuff like that in the bed of his truck) behind the truck and unloaded a lot of the sand, gravel and cement onto the tin. Then we unloaded the posts. I told Buff that I would stretch the chain between his truck and the Jeep and I wanted him to "ease the truck out of the ruts by gently rocking it back and forth." When David gave the signal, I started to pull. I looked out my side view mirrors and there was Buff spinning his tires; mud flying out the back like a speed boat barreling down the Tennessee River shooting rooster tails out the back.

I took the Jeep out of gear, got out and hollered for him to stop. I told him the spinning wasn't doing anything but burying him deeper in the mud. That he needed to ease the truck out of the ditch. I said let's try again but this time, "Go easy on the gas pedal." Again I looked in my rear view mirror and he had towers of mud spewing out the back of his truck. I took the Jeep out of gear and hollered at David, "Swap places with him!" When he got behind the wheel, I told David the same thing I had told Buff, "Now, gently start rocking the truck from forward to reverse. When you start to get some momentum going forward, I will pull you up out of the ditch." It took a couple of times but we did rock the truck out of the ditch. When we got it out, I didn't stop pulling until we were up on dry solid ground.

Moving that pile of sand, gravel and cement was a little trickier but we did get it moved over to the next set of anchor posts we were putting together. The rest of the summer was pretty boring; just the daily grind of building that fence around the farm.

Many seasons have come and gone but I will always remember the summers I spent playing "come with me," especially that summer before my senior year. I worked with Buffalo again the following summer, but that is the last I can remember working with him.

Buffalo was one of the great teachers that I've known.

I miss Buffalo and long for the days when we worked the hot summers together. The lessons he taught me through the game we played; don't be afraid of hard work. A little sweat and sore aching muscles never hurt anybody. These lessons have stayed with me all my life.

For years after that whenever I went for a job interview I told my interviewer about my summers playing "come with me," and how it gave me an appreciation for hard work and the rewards of sticking to a job until it's finished and done right.

Midnight Run

A Letter from Iraq

Sgt. Lindsay Freeland

I drive a truck in Iraq. We drive at night, so when most of my friends at home are sound asleep, I'm driving a heavy truck across the desert in Iraq. It's a pretty amazing scene, especially when I'm the front truck, and I can see this line of lights behind me. We're tightly packed in a convoy and we brighten up that whole night road. I always think of it that we're stringing through Iraq like Christmas tree lights. A bunch of white, big, bright lights snaking through the dark desert. And we usually are the biggest light out there, because not many Iraqis like to drive at night.

Sometimes there'll be Iraqis out there, but not too many of them. If we do see them, they're usually a lot nearer their own Iraqi rest stops, which are like their markets on the side of the road. Or it could be a fuel station—usually a tanker truck with a hose hooked to it tended by a little kid ready to fuel up to make money for the day. There will be markets behind the fuel station. They're just out in the middle of the desert, sometimes in the middle of nowhere. They're usually to the side of the road. It's their version a Starbucks, or maybe McDonald's.

We conduct our operations at night. It's our agreement with the Iraqis so that we don't interrupt their life as much—just because we are a really long and big convoy. They don't like us, and you can tell that. If we're headed northbound, the local traffic will be going both ways in the southbound lane. Because we have big cruiser weapons on our vehicles they don't want to be near us. We have bright lights.

We try to be nice and try to turn off the left side or something and dim the lights for them. Usually they just don't like being near us, so they'll pull off the road completely and just turn their flashers on and wait for us to pass.

I've done maybe 20 or 30 convoys since I've been here. It can become pretty mundane. Shorter missions of eight hour missions go really fast. The longest we've had is about 15 hours. It seems very, very long and drawn out, and your legs get pretty tired staying in that one position for a long time when you only have one stop throughout those 15 to 16 hours.

Our trucks are outfitted with a cooler filled with energy drinks next to the gunner's turret, and we just reach behind him, and grab a drink so by the end of mission our bladders are saturated. I think I drink probably about three energy drinks in one convoy. I realize that's not good, you know. Not good for you. But it helps. Especially on the boring convoys, and the long, long drawn out convoys.

We always have at least one or two breakdowns of our third country national supply trucks. I think on one 15-hour convoy we had probably about seven or eight breakdowns. It was ridiculous.

Sometimes when I'm driving or we're stopped, I almost forget where I am. Sometimes I feel like I'm driving in the desert of the U.S., maybe Arizona or something like that. It looks like a normal highway within the states and it's dark, and it's just a normal paved road. It's not kept up as well as roads in the states and half the road doesn't have stripes separating the lanes and marking the edges, but for the most part, it reminds you of a normal highway. Sometimes I feel like I'm on a long road trip at home. Sometimes I feel like I'm driving a big freight truck, as if I were a truck driver back home. But that feeling doesn't last long. Suddenly I'm jarred wide awake, lurching over a part of the road that's not there anymore with holes and boulders up to the truck's axles I now see the desert alive with shadows, moving among the hulks of abandoned jeeps, trucks, broken down wagons. The trash of war and neglect, the terrain is bathed by the light of a half moon filtered through the constant yellow, purple haze of dust. In the east a blush of coming sun signals another day. My eyes are heavy, my body aches. Right now what would I give for a long hot and cold shower, fresh, clean sheets and a mug of coffee. I think of home. I look down—wait, I have my body armor on. I'm still in Iraq.

Birddogs

Larry McGehee

Our family made a trek to the local animal rescue shelter to adopt a new cat, a successor to deceased and lamented Tommy and Friday. To get to the cat wing of the shelter, we had to go through the dog room; some of the dogs were hounds. The trip brought to mind a couple of years immediately after World War II when old Camp Tyson, the army post near my hometown, was the site for the national foxhound field trials. The thousands of acres that once teemed with soldiers were the gathering place for hundreds of foxhounds. Each had a number painted on its side for judging purposes. When they were in their pens, all howling at once, they could have drowned out an air-raid siren.

Foxhounds were special status symbols for southerners. They were once associated with the leisurely life of southern plantation owners and their sons, but after the Civil War, when plantations were gone, foxhounds stayed on. Every dirt farmer had at least one. Foxhounds were reminders of a way of life that was gone and for which a war had been fought. Foxhounds were also signs of social and economic ambitions, the faith that the South would rise again. Even when Herbert Hoover was promising "a chicken in every pot," the southerner was more interested in land for his hound.

Sometime after World War II, however, southerners became a little more realistic about their aspirations. They didn't give up on having hounds and on wanting to own the places on which to keep them, but they shifted to birddogs instead of foxhounds. You can't eat foxes. Or, if you can, you don't. But you can eat quail. And you don't need to ride a horse to hunt them. Birddogs are more practical than foxhounds. That gathering of hundreds of hounds at Camp

Tyson in the late 1940s was like a gathering of Confederate veterans in 1900: the passing of an era, the last link to the English gentry tradition of foxhunting that the South had copied for so long. It was a sign that a New South was rising, of two-car garages and pickup trucks instead of ten-horse stables.

Quail smothered in gravy is great for breakfast. In fact, now there were even quail farms where quail were raised in captivity like chickens for sale to restaurants. It sort of goes against the grain; they don't even need birddogs to catch them.

Without birddogs, there would be no birddog stories. It's a little like fishing. The tales are more important than the actual hunting or fishing which is really taxing and tedious work. We'd rather talk about it than do it. Some of the South's best stories, really superb replacements for the Uncle Remus tales, are birddog stories. William Faulkner's best words are his hunting stories, better even than his novels. He was a great hunter who enjoyed the campfire tales of other hunters more than he enjoyed pulling a trigger himself.

A typical birddog story will make one's dog out to be better than anyone else's. They run something like this one, about Zeke: one bragging bird hunter mercilessly bored everyone in the coffee shop crowd, talking about his bird dog. Finally one listener told him his dog couldn't hold a candle to one he knew of out in the country and took the braggart to see for himself. Out at a farm, they met an old farmer with a body gnarled with age and a chin stained with tobacco juice. The old man showed them his hounds, a dozen feisty yappers scampering around the dirt yard. The braggart asked to see the best one. "That'd be Zeke, that one over under the porch," the farmer said. He pointed to a dog that looked as old and crippled as himself. Then he called the dog, who shuffled over slowly, and they headed for the fields. Half way across the field, the old dog lazily pointed at a bush, and a covey of quail flew up; the braggart wasn't much impressed. Farther, they came to two bushes. The dog pointed to one with his paw and the other with his head. The brag-gart laughed at the dog's confusion, until a covey flew out of both bushes. A little farther on, the dog rolled over on its back, its feet in the air. The younger hunter laughed again, until a covey flew out of the tree overhead. Next the dog stuck its nose down a groundhog hole. The young hunter laughed. The dog barked once, took out its nose, and a covey flew out of the hole.

By now, the bragging hunter was beginning to concede defeat. Just then the dog pointed at another bush. Nothing flew out. The hunter laughed again. "See, there's nothing there at all," he said. "It's all been just luck." The farmer spit a long squirt of tobacco. "Just wait a second," he said. Just then a covey of quail flew into the bush. "Ole Zeke was just telling you where the birds were going to be." "I've got to have that dog," the convinced young hunter yelled. "Name your price." "Ain't for sale," said the farmer. "Besides, why would you want an old dog that's blind in both eyes?"

And that's why the South needs birddogs. We need to keep our tales from dragging.

Some folks are just natural hound collectors. I've never been that lucky. We went through a long line of beagles, cocker spaniels, and mutts when I was younger. They all ran away or died before we could get attached to them. I blame that—and a lot of other things—on my brother, who was bitten by a dog when he was about four and had to have rabies shots. They killed the dog. I always figured the dogs we got afterward knew that and wanted no part of us.

Closest I ever came to feeling kin to a hound was with Jip, my grandparents' sad-looking birddog that seemed to like to go BB-gun hunting with me out near their place. There was a great sand gully there that had grown up with pines and shrubs in the middle of old oaks and hickories. One October when I set it on fire by shooting some Halloween firecrackers in the sage field part.

I loved the trips to that old farm. You could tell it was old-style living; the hallway where Jip slept in most days used to be a dog-trot connecting the two main rooms that had functioning fireplaces and feather beds where company gathered day or night. Between the great food and the featherbed luxury were long, long hours that any boy could ways to fill.

Jip seemed to wake up when I visited, as if he spent most of his time sleeping in that hallway or under the wooden front porch waiting for me to arrive. He was already old when I came along, and those trips into the gully across the gravel road in front of the house must have stirred some memories of his from his own pup days.

I remember when I came to stay once and found Jip had died. The bachelor uncle who lived on the place took me across to the gully and showed me where Jip was buried. I went back that afternoon and collected sandstones from the gully and used them to outline Jip's grave, and I wrote his name with them in the center of the red rock rectangle.

I believe I still could find his grave today.

Footlocker II

Collected Poems of Love, War,
and Resurrection

What Is This Mystery?

This mystery called a word
And when laced together in a careful way,
Called language.
Today I leave you these scratches
On a rock and on the wind-swept dirt
To tell you how I feel
My secret thoughts of
Pain and joy
My dreams and fears,
Longing
How can this be?
These scratches and mischievous marks
Are only scratches and mischievous marks
Like shadows hiding from the sun.
How can this be?

September

I have held September in my arms,
Tasted her warm flavors with my tongue,
Admired her brown-orange leaves,
And savored the tart persimmon.
I've listened to the call of wild geese
Honking their way south
For the coming winter,
And once on a day in September
Knowing no better,
I walked all the way to the sky.

BENWICK'S WREN

Writing Is Like Building a Wood Box

Go into your shop
And build a plain wood box
As best you can.
Keep on going back
Day by day to make it better.
After a while—
Maybe a long while,
You'll be surprised to find
That your wood box has turned
Into a beautiful cabinet,
Maybe even a piece of art.
That's the way it is with writing
Just keep on keeping on.

Don't tell me,
show me.
Don't write about a river,
Be the river.
The secret of successful writing:
    The right word
    At the right place
    At the right time.
    But most of all the silence in between.

Poetry Is

"You want poetry?"
The old man asked.
"Write your own, ain't
No poetry police
Keeping you from it.
One thing to remember, though—
Poetry is
What it is
Nothing less
Nothing more.
Poetry speaks for itself if you'll only listen.
It is the sound of rushing water
When the river is high
Sounds of trains leaving in the night
Through tunnels of smoke and purple fog.
Long dark trains filled with faceless people
And what might have been.
That's what poetry is.
Or ought to be."

Let Me Be Who I Am

Degrees and awards, I find, are only for show
Placed on a vacant wall for some to see
As are medals on the chest.
Look—see what I've done,
Where I've been, look at me.
But who am I, really?
In the death of a quiet, black night
When devils come to call my name
And dance around my bed,
Who am I beneath my laughing mask?

I pray to the Gods, where ever they may be,
Let me defend myself.
Let me count the times I've found mystery
    in the quiet cathedrals of woods
Or by slow moving water and harvest fields.
Let me count the times I've fed the birds and field mice,
Picked goldenrod and Spanish needle.
Let me remember the songs and prayers
    I've heard in the wind,
The call of whippoorwills, frogs and doves.
I pray to the Gods
Let me walk my way and live my life
Like unmeasured lines.
Let me be me before I go.

May, 1944

On a Liberty ship, the Pittsburgh on the way to Scotland.
I recall the last sight of familiar land
    dropping into the ocean
With nothing left but flat water from horizon to horizon.
We're in a spell of good weather and I'm holding
Down most of the food,
Such as it is,
Spending every possible moment on deck.
I've seen a school of sharks, several whales,
    dolphins and flying fish.
Sometimes the water is still and quiet as a table top.
Sometimes restless, thoughtful or angry
Like days and nights during the storm,
Its color changing from green, blue, purple or red.
Tonight I'll watch the sunset again.
I'm drawn to the ocean in a way I can't understand.

Edinburgh, Scotland

With the signal of breaking dawn
Timeless moss covered castles
Emerge from the fog
To stand broad-shouldered on the dark hills
One more day.
This place
Holds all there is to know
About time, mystery, and castles,
Birds, seaweeds and fog.
One more day comes alive
With the sound of ships' horns
And the cry of hungry birds.

Tides Wash In,
Tides Wash Out

Alone
In my rock house by the sea—
Except for the giant turtles
Who come out at night
To lay their eggs.
Alone—except for the birds and crabs
The constant wind
And the music of the lapping waves.

An Indian Prayer

O' Great Spirit
Whose voice I hear in the winds,
And whose breath gives life to all the world,
Hear me! I am small and weak, I need your
Strength and wisdom.

Let me walk in beauty, and make my eyes
Ever behold the red and purple sunset.

Make my hands respect the things you have
Made and my ears sharp to hear your voice.

Make me wise so that I may understand the
Things you have taught my people.

Let me learn the lessons you have hidden
In every leaf and rock.

I seek strength, not to be greater than my
Brother, but to fight my greatest
Enemy—myself.

Make me always ready to come to you with
Clean hands and straight eyes.

You have noticed that everything an Indian does is in a circle, and that is because the Power of the World always works in circles, and everything tries to be round. In the old days when we were a strong and happy people, all our power came to us from the sacred hoop of the nation and so long as the hoop was unbroken the people flourished . . . Everything the Power of the World does is done in a circle. The sky is round and I have heard that the earth is round like a ball and so are all the stars. The Wind, in its greatest power, whirls. Birds make their nests in circles, for theirs is the same religion as ours. The sun comes forth and goes down again in a circle. The moon does the same, and both are round. Even the seasons form a great circle in their changing and always come back again to where they were. The life of a man is a circle from childhood to childhood and so it is in everything where power moves. Our tepees were round like the nest of birds and these were always set in a circle, the nation's hoop, a nest of many nests where the Great Spirit meant for us to hatch our children.

—*Hehaka Sapa (Black Elk)*

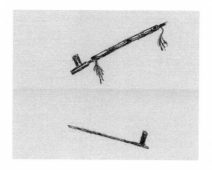

The River

Most of all I like the endless river,
Stretched as far as I can see.
I like the way moonlight plays on the water
The way it moves.
Always going somewhere.
If I should ever die,
Scatter my ashes from the big bridge
And I'll be happy the rest of the way.

A Cry from My Heart

We can never walk again in innocence
But we can grow in love and understanding
And acceptance.
Together we can walk in new fields
And down open roads and paths and woods.
There is so much beauty to share
But so little time
There is, however the eternity of now.
I wish for only peace in my life
To smell the rain
Watch sunrise and sunsets
And to see our children grow.
Is that too much to ask?

Letter from El, Thursday, August 1976
11:55 p.m. London, 5:55 p.m. CDT

The woman who lives in the stone house by the sea.

Over Light and Easy

You go away one more time,
I'll not be here when you get back.
She'd said it all before.
This time she meant it.

I'd do it all over again,
My life I mean,
And not change a thing—
Except leaving her.

Counting Stars

Last night after the summer storm,
The clouds gathered themselves
And stole away.
Then in awe I watched stars come out.
I counted them one by one
Shivering in excitement and wonder.

On Sanibel Isle

The touch of your hand,
The grace of your face,
The nearness of you,
Together we stand
Gathering white shells and wonder
Braced against the dawning of another day.

Argentina

Argentina
I love your gentle kisses.
I love your tan lines,
The curve of your hips,
The erotic beauty
Of you
Holding yourself
In the faded glow
Of the night's light.

The Baptizing

And again they came, that early Sunday morning,
A wet-dew August morning,
To beat the heat and prepare the way.
In the shade of the hackberry trees
Behind the church where red sumacs grow
We spread the bounty from the fields.
And sang songs with frogs and whippoorwills.
"Shall the Circle be Unbroken"
"In the Sweet-by-and-by."
Yonder stands my love,
Tall and tan in her wet, white dress.
Come walk with me, love, give me your hand.
Follow me deep into the cool water.
There among the ferns,
All of your sins, like summer memories,
Will be washed away.

Harms Methodist Church, built in 1915, was first organized in about 1839 when several different denominations combined for a union meeting, coming from great distances in wagons, on horseback, and on foot and camping during revivals one mile northwest of the present site. The church was known as Union Camp Ground.

Melissa

Wet north wind chills your name
Like the sound of some strange crippled bird
Croaking its song to a world that died in the night
When no one watched
And few cared.

In this summer hiding-place we played.
Built dreams and frog houses
Sand castles and old songs,
Collecting white shells to hold fragile memories.

Eternity embraced between then and now.
When you smiled—crossed your heart
And pledged your virgin vow.

Do you remember, Melissa?
I've lived with the night
A million years or more
Listening to the wind, whispering your name,
Melissa.

Normandy

Summer has come again
The lily of the valley blooms,
Meadow larks sing in the fields
While here on these cold sands, my brothers bled and died.
A soft summer day in early June,
Come with me I'll show you where Billy died.
Here on this awful shore.
See the shadows, the blood, the gore,
Hear the mad guns gone wild,
The wind choked with curses, and prayers.
One boy, a virgin still, throws down his rifle and screams.
Still they come in the boats; Look here's the very cliff
Where rangers climbed the ropes
The enemy shot them down one by one.
Still they climbed.
Now the guns are silent, grown cold not remembered.
On this day children have come to play
And build frog houses and castles
In the barren sand.
What year was that? You say.
Where, Normandy?
The silent waves will tell no more.

Whippoorwills

I don't know about God or mystery but I do
Know about quiet places and whippoorwills. It seems
To me if you've ever heard a whippoorwill cry
In the black of night, you've heard all
That you need to know.
Once I held a whippoorwill in my very hands
Warm, trembling, sparrow sized, brown in color.
It spoke to me, its voice chattering.
Many times I have listened to its lonesome mating call.
But that was a long time ago before the big war
When I was young but I remember still.

Fancy

This December morning
In a place where blue grass and thistles grow,
Alone in a cold wet grave
Near a place where she caught summer's sun
While holding court for blue birds and field mice,
I buried this majestic cat.

Her blood stained sable coat
Wrapped in an old shirt wet with my tears.
She will sleep here—unnoticed as season grow old
And children come to play.

Perhaps when spring comes again
(As many believe it will)
Some full-night
The wind will dance across the plain
And for a moment I will listen
In the hush . . . I will hear your name,

Fancy.

Come Home, Jimmy Rogers

I listen to the lonesome cry
Of freight trains running in the night and
Remember all the places I've seen,
Things I've done. So now
I sing your songs to chase the blues
While sleeping in the rain.
I'm a thousand miles away from home
Waiting for a train
I haven't got a nickel
Not a penny can I show.
I'm a rambling man on the endless rails
A crazy kid they call a hobo.

Even if a man might have had a dollar or two in his pocket, he sure wasn't going to waste it on a ticket. Better to swing onto a box car heading north or maybe ride his thumb. "I'll send for you soon as I find work and find us a place to live." And some did, others didn't. They left sometime during the night and were never heard from again.

The Wind

Dark comes early to my cabin
And a heavy quiet
As often happens before the coming storm
And in battle.
An early full moon hangs
Just out of reach
On the hill
Waiting
For the rockets to fall
Waiting and watching.
Tanks rumble in the distance,
Artillery streaks the far-sky.
And I wait
Surrounded by now
But wrapped in yesterday.
I am alone except for
The cries of the dying
And the careless wind
Talking to the trees.
The wind does not remember.
The wind does not care.

February Winds

February winds play games of hide-and-seek
with small black clouds that scurry
to find the amber sun,
casting shadows that etch memories
of a pig-tailed, brown-eyed girl,
holding still, two dolls, Hortense and George,
a calico cat and a wildflower.

Now she sings a love song to her first born
and whispers secrets that she learned
from an old house that sits silent
and listens to the February wind.

Blood River

I'm leaving in a couple of
hours, hitchhiking
to Blood River to get away
from the cable news.
However if the sky falls, I
expect to be one
of the last old coyotes left
standing. Presently
(Thank the Lord) I have a mate who
promises to be
at my side. Realistically
you know how that is:
Let the first coyote show up
in a new set of
wheels with the top down and music
on the radio
and there goes your dream. Anyway,
I have enough good
judgment left to follow my dad's
advice. "Son, go as
far back in the hills as you can
on a little piece
of land and stay away from the
government." So this
little piece of land is so far
off the beaten path
I can drink fresh running water
Out of my cupped hands.

Yesterday

So we come here again
To this sacred place
To remember our buddies
It was only yesterday
Yet you still hear the guns
Smell the smoke
Feel the cold
Taste the fear
From yesterday.

Ann Mariah's Path

Once my brothers and I
Followed Ann Mariah's path to the baptizing place
On Bloody River.
We threw rocks at snakes and frogs
And sang Amazing Grace.

    For the treasured memories of yesterday,
    For the exciting promise of tomorrow,
    But most of all for now.

June 2, 1944
Leicester

Dear Mom and Dad,

Just a quick note to let you know that I'm well and finally
settled at least for a little while. I'm attached to a general
hospital in Leicester, England but don't know for how long.
We've been running practically non-stop since we arrived
in Scotland. We're billeted in Quonset huts, Small rounded
metal buildings, cold but okay. The food is surprisingly
good, especially remembering what it was like on the ship.

I don't know how much of this will get by the cen-
sor—as if the Germans and Italians didn't know all that we
know anyway. There's a music and news radio show out of
Berlin we listen to almost every night with a sweet voiced
propaganda queen we call Axis Sally and she plays the very
latest hits from the states and briefs us with all the news.
She's always saying things like, "Go home, boys. Your
sweetheart is lonely. She needs you."

Well, it's June now but the weather's still cold, rainy
and mean. 55 degrees today, with fog and rain and a pale
sun once in a while.

I miss you and love you. Only wonder why it took me
this long to tell you. Please write every chance you have.
Our mail hasn't caught up with us yet. Just know that
I'm well and expect to be home some of these days. Dad,
we'll get us a bee outfit and plant some grapevines and sell
honey. You can't beat that.

Love, M.

This letter, photocopied victory mail, did make it home as did all of my mail as far as I know. This letter has waited in my footlocker these many years. Today I read the faded words and I'm back to the hurry up, critical days just hours before the invasion. The very ground shaking and vibrating, with heavy trucks, trains, and tanks running, marching troops, the sky black with droning planes. I remember thinking the whole world must be waiting and holding its breath.

Turns out it was. The date is etched in history, June 6, 1944. The word that early morning came from the BBC, "We now have confirmed reports from General Eisenhower's office, Allied naval forces supported by strong air forces began landing armies this morning on the Northern cost of France."

And that was all.

Michael Freeland, Berlin, 1945, after the war

Do Not Resuscitate

I sit by your bed and hold your hand
and wonder, do you know I'm here.

Your gasping breath and muted pulse
announce to me that death is near.

I talk to you of pastures green and waterfalls
and angels 'round.

Let go, I say, and run today.
No broken hip to slow you down.

A fleeting smile, a gentle sigh.
Now all is quiet, but your goodbye.

—*Marie Beddingfield, combat nurse*

Shellshock

His chart stated a diagnosis of schizophrenia.
Day after day, I watched him, locked in his own world.
Often I wondered, what does he see,
Whose voice does he hear as he marches,
March, march, march down the hall.

Then one day I met someone who had known Bill
Way back when.
"Oh, Bill," he said. "Bill was fine until World War II.
It's shellshock," he said. Bill's never been the same.

Shellshock, just the sound of it conjures up pictures of
Blood and pain. I can hear guns and cannons and calls of
Medic, medic, over here. Over here. Hurry!"
I see you, Bill, a look of fear and disbelief upon your face.
You are immobilized by the horror that surrounds you.
You could not fight that day. Bill, your gun remained silent.

You could not fight that day, Bill. But today
You fight that battle over again and again . . .

—*Marie Beddingfield, combat nurse*

Hear the words of Isaiah:
    Let us go out in joy and be led back in peace.
    The mountains and the hills before you
    Shall burst into song
    And all the trees of the field shall
    Clap their hands.

We must plant love in the garden of our life.
    There are many kinds of seeds in us, both good and
    bad. Some were planted during our lifetime, and some
    were transmitted by our parents, our ancestors, and
    our society. Our ancestors and our parents have given
    us seeds of joy, peace, and happiness,
    as well as seeds of sorrow, anger and so on.
        —TichNhat Hanh

All that we are
arises from our thoughts.
Speak or act with a pure mind and heart
and happiness will follow you
as your shadow,
unshakable.
        —The Buddha

Where your treasures are, there will your heart be also.
        —Jesus of Nazareth

Dearest favorite Dad,

This is not a poem only a plea for mercy. In case you are
wondering who the bleep ran off with the keys to your jeep,
it's I, honorable #1 son. I went to the hospital in it with
John Carey to see Kate on Sunday afternoon. When I got
back up here, I found I still had the keys. Since we were
making such a short trip, I thought I would keep your battery charged. Shouldn't leave it sitting idle so long. Honest,
the battery tends to run down. Anyway the keys are on the
mantle over the fireplace on the left by the lantern.

Hopefully still your,
Son?

Mickey Freeland in the
control room of WKTA-FM,
circa 1965

The Sacred Kitchen: Forbidden Fruit

Forgive me, Father, for I have sinned.
But in truth, Father, the woman made me do it,
With chocolate, black dreamy, full bodied.
The woman tempted me,
Her name is Chocolata.
Once upon a soft August morning
I was captured by the sweetness
Of her smile,
Her hard embrace,
Her panache (or is that the word for chocolate flavor?)

Deliver me, Father, from the temptation
Of this garden. Snakes and apples I can handle,
But the smell, the touch, the
Taste of chocolate
Is more than I can bear.

(In the year of Chocolate, 2009
John C. Campbell Folk School)

Normandy 1944

It is for those who died we sing
The swan-song of the great:
It is for those who wounded lay—
For those who kept the date;
It is for every one who went
To test the rules of fate:

We give them what is due each man
Who crossed that awful shore;
Who dared the flame of circumstance—
Defied the battle's roar
We hail who loved their lives not less
But loved their country more!

—*William L. Embry, 82nd Airborne*

I Am My Dog's Best Friend

I talk and Callie listens—
Or pretends, I can't be sure.
Sometimes I believe she reads my mind.
I say I am her master
She knows better but we both pretend.
So it is with love, I think.
Is it real—or pretend?
You never know until it's over.
Then you wonder—is it really over?
Callie and I walk on toward a full summer moon
And watch it disappear behind a cloud.
The night has turned dark, lost, empty
Like lost love when it goes away.

We Are One

I'm awake before good light
To hear the world come alive:
The thrill of katydids and whippoorwills
And owls.
One owl calls from
Down the hollow.
Soon one answers
From the hill.
These songs I love
But the silence more

      Come be with me
      Let me hold your hand
      Forever.
      We are one.

Today I will be content
With few words
Only today
Let me learn
From the sound
Of tumbling waters.
The traveling wind
And the awareness
Of now.

The Sound of Silence

In the hush
Of morning
In a warm valley
Called forget the sun.

In a gentle field
Surrounded by horizon
Quick night birds
And war gods,
She found peace
And forgiveness
And a perfect place to die.

"Forgive me, God," she said.
And that was all
Except for the cries of night birds
And the sound of silence.

My Love

My Love
Was there ever in all of time
A day like this? Just so:
Of all the other times
And all the other places
Will you remember . . .
Our last time?

Will you remember candlelight,
The taste of warm wine
The laughter and the tears,
The silence in between,
Will you not remember . . .
My name?

I Knew Hank

Left home before good daylight
Heading east toward Greenville
Up State Highway 93 to Kingsport
Out US 23 to Gate City to Big Stone Gap
And Appalachia on the trail of the Lonesome Pine.
On to bloody Harlan, a town lost in purple fog
Song, mystery, coal dust and legend.
Hank Williams rides with me all the way
On the radio. Like we were walking to the sky.

Kin Folks, a True Story

Tom Buchanan, Martha's youngest,
rode his little red mare home from the Civil War
singing all the way.
Big handsome man, liked women,
good times and sour mash whiskey.
(Women liked him, too.)

One night that spring, Tom went to a dance
and didn't come home.
Martha woke from a dream seein' Tom's little
red mare standin' under the cedars
shiverin' wet, muddy, head hanging down,
Saddle under her belly.

Martha got out of her bed, walked the floor til daylight
"Tom's drowned in Bloody River!"
When daylight came, she looked and there under
the trees stood the little red mare. Wet. Muddy.
Just like in her dream.

Tom sleeps now and will evermore under old cedars
near the river, where restless winds moan in the trees.
Every spring on full moon nights when
the river is wild and high, a little red mare comes and
waits by his grave.

Short Mountain

I've been to Short Mountain
And I've been to war.
They're each a bitch,
But in different ways.
I'm a tired old soldier so
I'll speak of war no more.
But Short Mountain's
Something else.
I can only bend and stretch
These words so far.
So come see for yourself.
One full moon night—or one sunset
Will show you what I mean.
Walk all the way to the top.
Breathe the cold fresh air.
Surround yourself
With the mystery near
Low slung purple skies,
Search the clouds long enough,
You'll find the invisible face of God.

A Song for Ada

I'd never seen
My grandfather cry
Until that first time
Under the dark cedars
When he carried wild roses
To Ada's grave.

I saw him sitting there on the red clay ground
Alone and silent
Talking to no one
But himself

I often wonder
What it's like in the long dark night
When he hears her voice calling his name—
Reaching to hold her,
To find only a cold empty place.

I often wonder:
Who do you hold when your love is gone?
Who's to share your life,
And sunsets and dreams
When your love is dead?

Someday

Someday
I'll come again
and write a poem about September,
not a tired song of lazy Indian summer days
or turning leaves dancing in the wind.

Let me write an honest poem
telling of our love
warm red wine
and the timeless magic of candlelight.

Someday
when you are gone
I'll come here again
in the deep night
to light candles
and remember September.

Memories

Life is filled with memories
Lived one moment at a time
Sacred moments
Joy
Pain
Sadness

But all precious
And gone too soon
Yet love remembers all.

I am the north wind.
My spirit rides these dark hills
Listening, seeking, remembering.

And I am the river.
Come look at me. Be still and listen to my song.
Come stay with me, and I will be your friend.

Shadows

I hide in the empty shadows
Alone
Invisible
Not remembered

Dancing flames shoot sparks of fireflies
While the old ones
Tell the old stories
One more time.

I watch as the hungry fire
Brands pictures in my mind.
Outside the howling wind wraps its fingers
Around the cold black night.

Simile:

> Her eyes mysterious and dark as the ocean at night
> Winds danced in the leaves like ghosts
> In the evening, smoke rose from the
>   barns like mist on the river.
> Storms lashed, winds howled like messengers from hell
> Buttercups kiss the morning tender as a lover's lips

Metaphors:

> He was a mountain
> She was springtime: April my favorite month
> The fields became my friends
> The lamps of early morning
> On patrol O'Doule was a silent panther

Personification:

> The innocent face of morning
> White birch sentinels guard the river
> Springtime is youth
> Autumn is an old man
> Laughing wind
> Heart of the poem/the poem's heart

Consonance:

> Pitter patter
> The wail of the wind.

Owl

Owl is crying forlornly in the dark,
I heard him calling to his mate last night.
I waited with him to hear the familiar answering cry,
And my heart fell with his
as the silence fell, louder than a cry.
He is still calling tonight,
only to be answered by longer silences.
I have never seen the owl.
I have only heard him calling
and waiting . . .

 —*Unknown*

To a Grandson at Graduation

I wish you many miles
Of open roads, top down
With wind in your face.
I wish you many pretty girls
(but not too many).
I wish you much success
(Whatever that is).
I wish you long life
And happiness
And a place to rest
When you come
To the end of the road.

Barn Swallows

One summer a pair of sparrow-sized barn swallows built their mud and grass nest under the roof of our porch. I patiently watched as they lined the nest with feathers and soft plant materials that soon held six brown spotted white eggs. For many days the parents took turns sitting on the eggs and guarding the nest. Until finally six small fuzzy birds pecked their way through the shells and perched on the side of their nest, impatiently waiting for the parents to bring gnats and bugs. When the little birds grew older, they took on the colors of the adults, upper parts dark steel blue under parts buff, throat and forehead rusty. Then I watched for the longest time as they sat fluffing their wings, preening themselves, waiting for more handouts and the courage to fly. One warm day, with much fuss, and constant twittering, they exploded from the nest, I thought that's the last of the barn swallows, but the next year two more returned to start another family.

I often think of that special time and wonder what intelligence brought these beautiful small birds to this protected place, safe from wind and rain. How did the little ones know when the time was right to fly?

What mystery brought them back to me?

Journal

September 30
From Paris to London

We're now approaching the English shore near Dover in a
C47 transport plane, my first plane ride. The pilot is a lieu-
tenant, about my age, wearing a sharp leather flight jackets,
collar turned up and a crushed go-to-hell cap. No tie. His
shirt collar unbuttoned. All this guy needs is a white silk
scarf around his neck and he'd look like a World War I
fighter ace. One other passenger, a major wearing a tanker's
jacket with the triangular 3rd army patch sits at the far end
of the plane. He looks as hung over as I feel.

I look off to the right through patches of fog and
clouds and see the famous chalk white cliffs drop all the
way to the blue-green waters of the English Channel and I
think of the song, *Blue Birds of Dover* . . . Peace will come
again someday and blue birds will fly over the white cliffs
of Dover.

Morning

First blush of sun
Paint the eastern sky
Holding still the early
Light.
Waiting its time
Waiting
To mark the morning.
The world waits
Silent.
Now comes the morning fire
Burning wet fog
Against the sky
And from the silent trees
Along the river.

Time and the Wind

The boy feels the chill of wind
Against his door
And hears it call his name,
Come play with me
The time is late.
Come play with me,
I'll carry you home.

I enjoy the feel of the axe handle. I swing the axe in a full arc, with a slight twist of the wrist at the point of impact; see the seasoned block of oak shatter into two parts. Gradually my mind and muscles loosen, my breathing deepens, and I enter a peaceful place I haven't felt for a long time. I'm one with the axe, at home as though I've never been away. Then a surprising thought enters my mind. Something is different. Where's the echo? Once echoes reverberated down the hollows and bounced against the hills to the sound of chopping. As late as 1943 when I left home, I distinctly remember my grandfather calling from a distance above the barns with his echoing voice calling me again and again.

This barn sits on land once owned by my great-grandfather Allen Durwood Freeland. I knew it as the "Bucklick," a place where deer came to find salt.

The Land

The land speaks to the soul:
The silence and smell of woods
After rain.
And the way the sky looks
At sunset
Or break of day.
Spring's first frogs singing
In the marshes.
The clear call of bob whites.
The morning dove.
You can keep all of your creeds.
Keep them all.
One walk in the woods
Or by the river
Is enough for me.

In the quiet evenings
    When shadows grow long
        And night birds cry
            You can still see smoke rise
                From the vine covered barns.

Time

Time is measured only
By the sun and moon.
You cannot rush
A season.
Each has its own way
Its own story to tell.
Spring brings the smell
Of new buds, leaves
And blossoms,
Fresh plowed ground
And the music of a million frogs
From the streams and marshes.
Songs and squawks of crows,
Blackbirds, hawks and
The rest.
Summer is growing time
That passes at its own
Sweet pace allowing cops
To ripen as they will.
Indian summer and fall
Is for gathering crops and apples,
Cutting wood, getting ready
For the long coming winter
But fall is sad because
Like the colors of the
Blazing sumacs, yellow maples
And hickories, it too
Will slowly but surely fade away.

Darkness comes early
to my Cabin

Pipe Smoke

You're gone.
The whine of tires is a faint echo.
Now only the frogs
Laughing in perfect compatibility
At my solitude.
There was so much to say,
It remains unsaid.
So much love to show.
But now there is only me
And the frogs
And pipe smoke.

—*Stephen Allen Freeland*

Ode à mon père
(pour son anniversaire)

The lonely echo of swift tires I hear,
Which sweep away on a bare road, empty but
    for the April song of winter's tear.
Spring's frogs, my mute guest, sing of fertility
And mock my solitude of sterility.

Leaving nature's walls of sylvan antiquity
I enter in the silent bounds of night's cloak—
These unyielding walls that close about me.
Here a misty voice to me sings sadly
A thin veneer of past presence—pipe smoke.

    —Stephen Allen Freeland

    Dear Dad,
    This is an ode on which I have worked. It is
    not finished but I thought I would send you
    this much for your birthday. I have taken the
    idea from the little piece I wrote while living
    at the cabin. All that I could remember about
    that poem was the frog's symphony and the
    pipe smoke.
        Steve

Coming Home

Down,
    Down,
        Hidden low between the mountains
Is an obscure field,
The site of a battle.

There, in the valley, are two soldiers,
One bearing a dying one upon his back.
Two soldiers plodding their way,
On a dank, dark, cold autumn night.

    Whistling through the trees,
    Whipping across their path
    The wind breathed his carol,
"Come, come run with me,
Through the woods and fields.
Come feel my life,
Come savor my meal.

    Said the dying,
"Did you hear,
Did you hear the call?
Did you feel the sensation as he pulled?"

"Surely," thought the living,
    "He is delirious in his pain
    Not only does his wound pierce his body
    But his mind also."

"Hush," said he, "Soon, soon we'll be home,
　　There you'll find solace,
　　There your torture shall be quaffed
　　The burden of your pain lightened."

"Come. Come. Steal away with me.
Travel to your most desired dream.
I'll tell you my story
I'll relieve your tortured soul,
Relieve it to a solace of velvet cushion."

"There, did you not hear?
Did you not hear his call?
Did you not taste the beauty of his song?
Were you not swayed by the strings of his spell?"

"Hush. Soon, soon we'll be home
　　There a warm fire waits
　　There a soft bed is readied
　　There your torment shall be attended."

"Now, now is the time to abide in me!
Quit the earth that binds you!
Leave the grasp of your figure
And come, come run with me
Through the woods and the fields."

"There, did you not hear?
Are you not of wont to reply
To a beckon that pulls so strong?
Does the whispered elegance not tingle your soul?
Does his resonant beauty not fill you with desire?"

"Hush, soon, soon we'll be home
    Your wound will be healed,
    Your mind will be eased."
Then, as his burden was lightened,
He tightened his grip
And lurched on.

Down
    Down
        Hidden low between the mountains
In an obscure field,
The site of a battle.
There, in the valley
In the dank and dreary darkness
Is a lonely soldier, bearing a corpse upon his back.
A soldier with a corpse upon his back
Plodding his way in the cold autumn night.

    —Stephen Allen Freeland
    March 2, 1954–September 2, 1979

Homecoming

To this haunted place I return
To our valley of yesterday
Where we knew love and wildflowers
Black-eyed susans and the summer rose.

In the valley, before I rest
And sleep among the pines,
Come again and hold me
Hold tight sweet memories, dead
Like winter's lilac,
Crushed like summer's rose.

—*Michael Freeland*

In the Garden

Sirius seethes sour in the mid-afternoon sun.
In the disheveled garden the Johnson grass
Chokes the last of the spring crocuses.
The putrid scorched scent of ragged weeds
And surging wisteria crowd for your attention.
The young wife sitting in her cluttered garden
Stoops into a half-moon gesture—her curved breasts
And thighs turning for the scathed earth—
And gathers a solitary prudent beauty;
The butter cup, or naked lady, covered
By the burning stench of Johnson grass.

—*Stephen Allen Freeland*

Mother's Day

I could give you flowers,
    Blue, yellow, green or red.
Or I could give you jewelry
To please your heart instead.

I could take you places,
    But what have your eyes not seen?
So, what do I give you?
I give you love and hope and a dream.

I give you my love,
    All for you to keep,
And I give you a dream
    To comfort you as you sleep.
And I give you hope,
Knowing that your goal for me is never to sleep.

You see, Mom, just for you,
    My funds I could easily choke
But all that's meaningless without love.
And, besides, I'm broke.

—*Stephen Allen Freeland*

Song of the Sands

You are at best angels fallen,
Who are not good enough to be
Forever saved, nor bad enough
To be forever lost in
The voiceless fog of Sybil's dream.
You are at worst most sterile things,
Who are not bad enough to be
Forever lost; nor good enough
To be forever chained against
The hopeless fire of Zeus' rock.

—*Stephen Allen Freeland*

Lillian

Well, I just strolled around
Up to the old home
One Sunday day.

Well, no
That's not so
I came to mow her yard.

Well, I pushed that awkward machine,
Pushed that yellow thing
From the gravel onto her multi flowered lawn.

And then. . . . .
She came from around the back of the house,
A thin small black frame
Cast against white.

"I've come to mow your yard," I said,
Feeling big.

She gave no answer.
It was
Sunday day.

"Or would you wish I wait?" I said
Feeling small.

"You know what the Lord say
About working on a Sunday.
You can if you want to."

I wasn't doing her any favors.
So we sat on the porch.

And talked

She talked,
"The Lord giveth and.
The Lord taketh away."

She said, looking at nothing
And with a lisp
And a weak tremble,
Hiding a sly smile.

—*Stephen Allen Freeland*

Love Song

If love knew where some strangers keep
    Within deep walls an unquiet bird,
Perhaps sometimes into our cage
    That love would watch.

If love knew what some secrets yield;
    The sense, the thrill, the taste of love;
Perhaps sometimes that love would pause
    Before our wall.

If love knew where rich silence steals;
    Disguise her cries (the stolen breath);
Perhaps sometimes that love would wait;
    Bestow her eyes.

If you knew how one loves you true,
    And if you knew how much,
Perhaps sometimes our love would will
    Her gentle touch.

—Stephen Allen Freeland

Beekeeper: The Last Romantic
(For Grandpa Mason from your Grandson)

Wind sings and dances in the leaves
And courts the blossomed apple tree,
Below them you who mates the bee.

About the bees, among the trees
From hives you've built you draw
The sweet drink of the God, And He
In name divine weeps not for all
The monstrous rustling of the leaves.
And what care you, who loves the bee.

—*Stephen Allen Freeland*

Notes

Dear one,
This has been a long
And lonesome day.
I missed our coffee
And touching you.
If somehow we should
Miss each other today,
Only know I love you
And long to be with you.

My life is filled
With joyous memories
Of times we've shared
Of shells we've found,
Treasure more precious
Than gold.
I cherish each moment
But none more
Than now.

—*Ellen Freeland*

As long as the moon shall rise,
As long as the rivers shall flow,
As long as the sun shall shine,
As long as the grass shall grow.
—*Common expression for terms of
treaties with Native Amerians.*

We shall overcome, we shall overcome,
We shall overcome some day.
Oh, deep in my heart I do believe
We shall overcome some day.
—*Old religious song adapted for the
1960s Civil Rights movement.*

War is not healthy for children
and other living things.
What if they gave a war and nobody came.
—*Popular 1960s slogans.*

Life is short and war is long.
—*Bartender at Leicester's Blue Pub,
or was it the Bull's Head?*

The Obituary

It is with regret
That we make
The following announcement:
He died today
Much to his considerable astonishment
And keen dismay
This corporate many-faced fellow
Organizer of vast pretensions
With little wit
And many tensions.

So weep not Rotarians,
Elks,
Roosters
Or committee.
Contain your glee.
Suppress your pity.

That's all and he was gone.
The end.

—*Michael Freeland*

Steve's Poem

There are no glazed monuments,
Only rocks
His rocks,
Him.
And his final expression
His wooden core
Grows
Unique and fast

Clean and
Selfish and
Pure.

Secrets

What do you see?
Tell me what you're thinking.
You excited?
Me too.
Look, a whole world out there
Just waiting.
A pretty world.
Stay close to me, little sister,
We've got a long way to go.

James and Amelia Hood, 2011

I waited until the last day to tell my sweetheart goodbye.
The day was wet with showers but warm with a gentle wind
from the valley. We parked near the road at Red Top hill
and walked, holding hands, the quarter mile or so through
the woods to the rock bluff overlooking the valley, took
shelter from the showers under heavy old cedar trees—a
private world walled by fog and mist. She was laughing
with tears and makeup streaking her face. We didn't have
to say goodbye. We just knew.

Mike, high school junior,
on Love's Lane, Red Top Hill.

And again they came, that early
Sunday morning
A wet, dew August morning
To beat the heat and prepare the way.

Mike Freeland at the Freeland cemetary,
grave of Robert Daniel Freeland

High school graduation picture of Ellen's mother,
Amy Flora Meeks Elmore

Mike's mother, Wilby Lee Murphy, and her brother
Randolph "Pete" Murphy, circa 1914.

Steve's Song

Too many Septembers have come and gone,
Too much water has run under the bridge,
Too often I remember the shadows of yesterday.
Now yesterday has come again
Here in this quiet garden of death
Where sumacs bloom
And the wind blows free
I am alone with the wind,
A wind that sings and dances in the leaves
Steve's metaphor, the wind—
His song, a song
That ended too soon.

Ode à mon père
(pour son anniversaire)

The lonely echo of swift tires I hear,
which sweep away on a bare road, empty
But for the April song of winter's tear.
Spring's frogs, my mute guest, sing of fertility
And mock my solitude of sterility.

~~I have~~ Leaving nature's walls of sylvan antiquity
I enter in the silent bounds of night's cloak —
These unyielding walls that close about me.
Here a misty voice to me sings sadly
A thin veneer of past presence — pipe smoke.

Dear Dad,

This is an Ode ~~that~~ on which I
have worked. It is not finished but
I thought I would send you
this much for your birthday. I have
taken the idea from the little
piece that I wrote while I was living
at the cabin. All that I could remember
was the frog's symphony and
the pipe smoke.

about that poem →

Steve